Mystery Mob
and the
Big Match

Roger Hurn

Illustrated by
Stik

RISING★STARS

Rising Stars UK Ltd.
22 Grafton Street, London W1S 4EX
www.risingstars-uk.com

The right of Roger Hurn to be identified as the author of this work
has been asserted by him in accordance with the Copyright,
Design and Patents Act 1988.

Published 2007
Reprinted 2008

Cover design: Button plc
Illustrator: Stik, Bill Greenhead for Illustration
Text design and typesetting: Andy Wilson
Publisher: Gill Budgell
Publishing manager: Sasha Morton
Editor: Catherine Baker
Series consultant: Cliff Moon

British Library Cataloguing in Publication Data.
A CIP record for this book is available from the British Library

ISBN: 978-1-84680-221-8

Printed in the UK by CPI Bookmarque, Croydon, CR0 4TD

Mixed Sources
Product group from well-managed
forests and other controlled sources
www.fsc.org Cert no. TT-COC-002227
© 1996 Forest Stewardship Council

Contents

Meet the Mystery Mob   4

Chapter 1: We're All Going to Wembley   7

Chapter 2: Stop Thief!   14

Chapter 3: More Trouble   19

Chapter 4: Monkey Business   26

Chapter 5: Going Bananas   32

Extras!

About the author   39

Fantastic football quiz   40

When I was a kid …   42

Adi's favourite football joke   43

How to be a footballer   44

Five fascinating football facts   46

Football lingo   47

Meet the Mystery Mob

Name:

Gummy

FYI: Gummy hasn't got much brain – and even fewer teeth.

Loves: Soup.

Hates: Toffee chews.

Fact: The brightest thing about him is his shirt.

Name:

Lee

FYI: If Lee was any cooler he'd be a cucumber.

Loves: Hip-hop.

Hates: Hopscotch.

Fact: He has his own designer label (which he peeled off a tin).

Name:

FYI: Rob lives in his own world – he's just visiting planet Earth.

Loves: Daydreaming.

Hates: Nightmares.

Fact: Rob always does his homework – he just forgets to write it down.

Name:

Dwayne

FYI: Dwayne is smarter than a tree full of owls.

Loves: Anything complicated.

Hates: Join-the-dots books.

Fact: If he was any brighter you could use him as a floodlight at football matches.

Name:

Chet

FYI: Chet is as brave as a lion with steel jaws.

Loves: Having adventures.

Hates: Knitting.

Fact: He's as tough as the chicken his granny cooks for his tea.

Name:

Adi

FYI: Adi is as happy as a football fan with tickets to the big match.

Loves: Telling jokes.

Hates: Moaning minnies.

Fact: He knows more jokes than a jumbo joke book.

We're All Going to Wembley

It's Cup Final day.
The Mystery Mob have tickets
for the match. They can't wait
for it to start. Gummy, Dwayne,
Chet and Adi support United,
but Lee and Rob are City fans.

Adi   Hey Rob, what's the difference
           between United and a drum?

Rob   I don't know.

Adi   You can beat a drum
           but nobody can beat United!

Rob   You wish.

Lee   Hey Adi, Rob and I call United's striker the wonder striker.

Rob   Yeah, we wonder how come he's so useless!

Adi   Grrrr!

Dwayne You know, I'd love to stand here all day joking with you lot, but we've got a game to watch.

9

Chet   So what are we waiting for?

Gummy Let's go.

There's a massive crowd outside
the ground, and Rob and Lee
soon get split up from the others.

Rob   Where are the others?
            I think we've lost them.
            I wanted to wish them luck – not.

Lee   Don't worry. We'll go to the office
            and ask them to put out
            a message on the tannoy
            telling the others not to look
            for us – we'll meet up with
            them by the Bobby Moore
            statue after the game.

Rob and Lee go in through the turnstiles
for the City fans. The inside of the
stadium is massive, and Rob has no idea
which way to go.

Rob   Er … where's the office?

Lee   Hmmm, it's along this corridor.

Rob   Hey, how do you know
stuff like that?

Lee   It's easy. There's a sign with a big arrow on the wall behind your head. It says: 'To the Office'.

The boys run down the corridor and up the stairs, following the signs to the office.

② Stop Thief!

At the top of the stairs the boys find another long corridor with lots of doors.

Rob I wonder which one is the office?

Lee It'll say on the door.

The boys walk along the corridor reading the signs on the doors. Then Lee stops suddenly.

Lee What was that?

Rob What was what?

Lee I thought I heard a noise coming from this room here – the Trophy Room. It sounded like something heavy falling over.

Rob You're right! I can hear someone moving around in there.

Lee The Trophy Room – hey, that's where they keep the FA Cup!

Rob So ... do you think someone's trying to pinch it?

Lee Well, there's only one way to find out.

TROPHY ROOM

The two boys creep up to the door
and pull it open. It's very dark inside
the room. Before they can switch on
the light to see what's going on, something
leaps out of the shadows and knocks
them over.

They pick themselves up and dash back
out of the room. But all they can see is
the big silver Cup vanishing round
the corner.

Rob   Wow! Did you get a look at the thief?

Lee   No. I only saw his hand. But I think he's wearing a fur coat.

Rob   What makes you say that?

Lee   Well, there's all this brown hair on the floor.

Rob   Hey, that's a clue.

Lee   What do you mean?

Rob   Well, all we've got to do is look for someone wearing a hairy brown coat with lots of bits missing, and that'll be the thief.

Lee   No, all we've got to do is look for someone carrying the FA Cup. And he's got a head start on us – so let's move.

③

More Trouble

At that moment, a man comes along
the corridor. He looks important.
He also looks surprised to see
Lee and Rob standing outside
the Trophy Room. He glares at them
and strides into the room.

Lee He's come to fetch the Cup.

Rob But it's been stolen.

Lee Right. And he'll think we took it.

Rob But we didn't.

Lee   I know that, but he'll never believe us.

Rob   So what are we going to do?

Lee   We're going to have to catch the thief ourselves. And we've got to do it before the match starts.

Rob   Why?

Lee   Because if we don't we'll miss the game. And anyway – what if City win and there's no Cup to give them?

Rob   You're right. That would be terrible.

Lee   Only one thing could be worse.

Rob   What's that?

Lee   We find the Cup and United win.

Rob   (shocked) Don't even think that.

The boys hear a roar of rage
from the Trophy Room. Then the man
in the jacket and tie storms out
into the corridor. His face is red
with anger.

Man   You! Boys! What have you done
             with the FA Cup?

Lee We didn't touch the Cup, honest.
But we saw the thief who took it.

Rob No we didn't. But we did see
his fur coat and one of
his hands.

Man What? Are you mad, boy?
You're in big trouble,
the pair of you. Just stay there
while I phone for the police.

Rob   Sorry. No can do.
We've got a thief to catch.

Lee   Don't worry. You wait here.
We'll be back soon with the Cup
and the real thief. Then you can
hand him over to the cops.

4

Monkey Business

The boys race off hot on the trail
of the thief. Soon they find themselves
outside a small gym.

Lee   This must be where the players
come to warm up.

Rob   But they're all out on the pitch
waving to the fans at the moment.

Lee   So the gym should be empty –
but I can hear someone inside.

Rob   Yes, and look! There's another long, brown hair on the door handle. Maybe we've tracked the thief down at last.

They step inside the gym.
Rob can't believe his eyes.

Rob   There's the thief, sitting on that exercise bike.

Lee   It's Chuckles – United's pet mascot. And he's got the FA Cup on his head!

Most clubs have people dressed up
as animals for their mascots,
but United's mascot is a real orang-utan.

Lee   He must have given his keeper
the slip when the teams went out
on to the pitch. But how are we
going to make him hand over
the Cup to us?

Rob   I know. I'm smarter than
a monkey. I'll ask him who's
going to win the game and then,
while he's thinking about it,
I'll grab the Cup.

Lee   Brilliant! But there's just one
thing wrong with your plan.

Rob   What's that?

Lee   Orang-utans don't speak English.

Rob   So what are we going to do?

Lee   No problem. Orang-utans love
            bananas. We'll swap him
            a bunch of bananas for
            the FA Cup.

Rob   But where are we going to get
            a bunch of bananas from?

Lee   United's changing room.
All footballers have bananas
at half-time. Bananas give them
energy for the second half.
So they're bound to have loads
in there.

Rob   Changing rooms – here we come!

5

Going Bananas

The boys return from United's changing room with a big bunch of bananas.

Rob   Oh no. Chuckles is on top of the wall bars! How did he get up there?

Lee   Duh, he's an orang-utan, not a hot-air baboon – he climbed. So you'll just have to climb up after him.

Rob   I can't climb up carrying
a bunch of bananas. I need to
use both hands.

Lee   No you don't. If Chuckles
can do it, then so can you.

Rob   Are you trying to make
a monkey out of me?

Lee   No. You can do that
all by yourself.

Rob tries to climb up the wall bars.
He has the bunch of bananas
tucked under his arm.

Lee   Keep going. You're nearly there.

Rob   Here you are, Chuckles.
Give me the FA Cup
and I'll give you these bananas.

Lee   Great! He's giving you the Cup.
Let him have the bananas.
But don't forget to hold on to
the bars with one hand,
or you'll ...

Rob   AAAARRRGHHHH!!!!!!!!!!!!!!!!!!!!

BOING! Rob falls from the top
of the wall bars, but he lands
on a trampoline. He bounces
up and down like a rubber ball.
The FA Cup flies out of his hands,
but Lee dives and catches it.

Rob   Great save!

Lee   Too right. And if City ever need a new goalie, they know where to find me.

Rob   You wish! Now if I can just stop
bouncing, we can put the Cup
back where it belongs.

Lee   Good plan. And if we hurry
we'll still get to our seats in time
for the kick off!

About the author

Roger Hurn has:

- been an actor in 'The Exploding Trouser Company'
- played bass guitar in a rock band
- been given the title Malam Oga (wise teacher, big boss!) while on a storytelling trip to Africa.

Now he's a writer, and he hopes you like reading about the Mystery Mob as much as he likes writing about them.

Fantastic football quiz

Questions

1 How did Wembley Stadium get its name?

2 How many players are there in a football team?

3 What is the person in charge of a football match called?

4 Why do lots of footballers eat bananas at half-time?

5 Which is the best position to play in if you want to win lots of caps for your country? Goalkeeper, midfielder or striker?

6 Which football team plays at Old Trafford?

7 Which football team's nickname is 'The Gunners'?

8 When the World Cup was stolen in 1966 which animal found it again? (Clue – it wasn't an orang-utan!)

Answers

1 It's named after the London Borough of Wembley where it is built.
2 There are eleven players in a football team.
3 A referee is in charge of a football match.
4 To give themselves energy – they'd have to be bananas not to eat them.
5 Goalkeeper. England, Wales and Northern Ireland's most capped players are goalkeepers.
6 Manchester United plays at Old Trafford.
7 Arsenal's nickname is 'The Gunners'. They sound like a team of hot shots!
8 Pickles the dog. Pickles saved the cup when it was in a pickle!

How did you score?

✋ If you scored all eight answers correct then you have golden boots – you're a top striker!

✋ If you got six answers correct you're a goal-scoring midfielder.

✋ If you got fewer than four answers correct you'll have to spend a bit more time training before you're ready for the big match.

When I was a kid

Eleven-year-old Ben is a big football fan and he loves the Mystery Mob's Big Match story. Here he gets to ask Roger some questions.

Ben   Did you play football when you were a kid?

Roger   Yes.

Ben   What was your team called?

Roger   Nottso Athletic.

Ben   Why were they called that?

Roger   Because we weren't very fit.

Ben   What position did you play in the team?

Roger   I was a striker.

Ben   So did you score lots of goals?

Roger   No, I didn't score any.

Ben   Why was that?

Roger   Because I was always on strike.

Adi's favourite football joke

Why is Cinderella hopeless at football?

Because she keeps running away from the ball.

How to be a footballer

Must-dos and don'ts

⚽ Play the game because you love it.

⚽ *Wear fancy football boots – they won't make you play better but you'll look good.*

⚽ Practise your ball skills every day.

⚽ *Work on your goal celebrations.*

⚽ Eat lots of fruit, vegetables and pasta and drink plenty of water.

⚽ *Learn to like playing in the pouring rain and freezing cold.*

⚽ Remember, football is a team game – so don't hog the ball.

⚽ *Make sure you have a cool haircut but don't let it stop you from heading the ball – even if it's muddy.*

⚽ Work on keeping fit.

⚽ *Try not to let the other team kick you –*
it hurts!

⚽ Don't pick the ball up with your hands –
unless you're the goalie.

⚽ *Always try your hardest but don't be*
a bad loser – learn from your mistakes
and play better next time.

⚽ Wear shin pads – the colour doesn't matter,
but the amount of padding does.

Five fascinating football facts

1 When football first started, you could have any number of players in a team – 500 a side was not unusual! There were hardly any rules.

2 Football as we know it was first played by children at posh public schools in England.

3 Notts County are the oldest football club. They were founded in 1862.

4 England won the World Cup in 1966. It's the only time they have won it.

5 Football is the world's most popular game. More people play it and watch it than any other sport.

Football lingo

Booking This is what you may get if you foul another player. But if you lose your temper and see red, you'll end up with a red card and be sent off.

Foul This happens when you deliberately kick, trip or push another player. (Unless your mum is the referee – then it's just an accident and not a foul.)

Hat trick This is when you score three goals – not when you pull a rabbit out of a top hat.

Headless chicken This is a player who runs about all over the pitch but is totally useless and never does anything with the ball.
(Just like the referee.)

Marking When you mark a player you try to stop them getting the ball. It doesn't mean you write on them with a felt pen.

For mail order information
please call Rising Stars on 0871 47 23 010
or visit www.risingstars-uk.com